LANGUAGE ARTS

CONTENTS

Author: **Betty Wilke Hudman**

Editor-in-Chief: **Richard W. Wheeler. M.A. Ed.**

Editor: **Helen Robertson Prewitt, M.A. Ed.**

Consulting Editor: **Larry L. Howard, Ed.D.**

Revision Editor: **Alan Christopherson, M.S.**

Alpha Omega Publications®

804 N. 2nd Ave. E., Rock Rapids, IA 51246-1759

EFFECTIVE COMMUNICATION

Communication is a two-way activity. You communicate with others when you write or speak. Others communicate with you when you listen or read.

Effective communication depends upon many of the skills that you will learn and practice in this LIFEPAC®. You will learn to write four types of sentences. You will learn the two most common sentence errors and both how to avoid them and how to correct them. You will have an opportunity to combine a variety of sentences to form paragraphs. You will learn how to recognize and avoid two common paragraph flaws. All of these skills will assist you not only in writing but also in your reading as well.

You will learn the importance of careful, correct pronunciation. You will discover some of the phonetic difficulties in pronouncing the English language. You will have an opportunity to practice pronouncing actual words as well as delightful "nonsense" words and tongue twisters. Skills acquired in speaking carefully also will help you to become a better listener.

The advantages of being able to communicate effectively with others carry over to all areas of your life, in and out of school. Effective communication is essential for a Christian young person who wishes to give testimony to his faith.

OBJECTIVES

Read these objectives. The objectives tell you what you will be able to do when you have successfully completed this LIFEPAC.

When you have finished this LIFEPAC, you should be able to:

1. Explain the importance of the sentence as a basic structure of communication.
2. Demonstrate "sentence sense" in recognizing a complete thought.
3. Classify and punctuate sentences according to function.
4. Identify three common sentence errors.
5. Spell new words.
6. Identify and explain inductive, deductive, and transitional paragraphs.
7. Explain and identify sequence and unity.
8. Explain certain dictionary and pronunciation facts.
9. Explain various types of nonsense literature.
10. Define certain literary terms.

Survey the LIFEPAC. Ask yourself some questions about this study. Write your questions here.

_____

_____

_____

_____

_____

_____

_____

_____

_____

_____

I. WRITING SENTENCES

A sentence is a group of words that expresses a complete thought and that is punctuated as an independent unit. In the written English language, the sentence is the basic structure. Until you have mastered the skills of writing clear, concise, correct sentences, you will not be ready to write paragraphs.

You will need to develop a "sentence sense" that enables you to recognize a complete thought in sentence form. You will learn to classify sentences according to their function.

In this section you will learn to write and to correctly punctuate declarative, interrogative, imperative, and exclamatory sentences. You will learn to recognize and to correct the three most common sentence errors. You will learn to pronounce and to define words and terms essential to the study of sentences.

The sentence skills you acquire not only will assist you in effective written communication. They will also help to apply clear thinking to sentences that you study or read for pleasure.

SECTION OBJECTIVES

Review these objectives. When you have completed this section, you should be able to:

1. Explain the importance of the sentence as a basic structure of communication.
2. Demonstrate "sentence sense" in recognizing a complete thought.
3. Classify and punctuate sentences according to function.
4. Identify three common sentence errors.
5. Spell new words.

VOCABULARY

Study these words to enhance your learning success in this section.

abstract (ab' strakt). Expressing a quality or idea rather than a particular object.

auxiliary verb (og zil' yur ē vėrb). Helping verb; verb used to form the tense of other verbs.

declarative (di klar' u tiv). Making a statement; explaining.

exclamatory (ek sklam' u tôr' ē). Spoken suddenly in surprise; expressing strong feelings.

function (fungk' shun). The work or normal action performed; the purpose.

imperative (im per' u tiv). Urgent; expressing a command or a request.

interrogative (in´tu rog´u tiv). Asking a question.

> **Note:** All vocabulary words in this LIFEPAC appear in **boldface** print the first time they are used. If you are unsure of the meaning when you are reading, study the definitions given.

> **Pronunciation Key:** hat, āge, cãre, fär; let, ēqual, tėrm; it, īce; hot, ōpen, ôrder; oil; out; cup, pút, rüle; child; long; thin; /TH/ for then; /zh/ for measure; /u/ represents /a/ in about, /e/ in taken, /i/ in pencil, /o/ in lemon, and /u/ in circus.

SENTENCE TYPES

Sentences may be classified, or typed, according to structure (as you learned in Language Arts LIFEPAC 704) or according to **function**. In this section you will study sentences according to their purpose, meaning, or function.

To review briefly, a sentence is a group of words that communicate a complete thought. A sentence is punctuated as a separate unit. A sentence begins with a capitalized word and ends with a period, a question mark, or an exclamation mark.

According to meaning or function, sentences may be placed in one of four different classifications.

A **declarative** sentence tells something about the subject. The proper end punctuation is a period. The declarative sentence is by far the most common in written English.

An **interrogative** sentence asks a question. The proper end punctuation is a question mark.

An **imperative** sentence expresses a command. The proper end punctuation is usually a period.

An **exclamatory** sentence expresses strong feeling. The proper end punctuation is an exclamation mark.

Read the following sentences. In the blank after each sentence, write the correct sentence type according to function.

Example: Why was Saul going to Damascus? <u>interrogative</u>

1.1 Saul of Tarsus was a Pharisee. _____

1.2 He was a bitter enemy of all Christians! _____

1.3 As he neared Damascus, he was blinded by a great light. _____

3

1.4	He heard a strange voice.	_____
1.5	"Saul, why do you persecute me?"	_____
1.6	At first, Saul did not understand what was happening to him.	_____
1.7	"Lord, what will you have me to do?" he asked.	_____
1.8	"Arise, and go into the city."	_____
1.9	For three days, Saul lay in darkness.	_____
1.10	The Lord appeared to a Christian named Ananias.	_____
1.11	"Arise, and go into Straight Street."	_____
1.12	"Ask for Saul of Tarsus."	_____
1.13	Ananias asked, "Is this the same Saul who persecutes the Christians?"	_____
1.14	"Go, for I have chosen this man to be my special vessel."	_____
1.15	Ananias proved to be a true Christian friend.	_____
1.16	Saul's sight was restored.	_____
1.17	He proclaimed Christ as the Son of God!	_____
1.18	The elders of Damascus were astonished at Saul's conversion.	_____
1.19	They asked, "Has this man gone mad?"	_____
1.20	Saul remained in Damascus for a time, preaching and teaching about Jesus Christ.	_____

Declarative sentences. The preceding sentences, when read in sequence, tell a story. Notice that half of the sentences are declarative. In most examples of written English, half or more of the sentences are declarative,

Declarative sentences *declare.* They may tell, explain, state, describe, define, or illustrate.

Write five declarative sentences. Remember to begin each sentence with a capital letter. Use the proper end punctuation.
Example: Spring wildflowers cover the hills.

1.21	_____
1.22	_____
1.23	_____
1.24	_____
1.25	_____

Interrogative sentences. If declarative sentences are so important, why are the other three types needed? Could the story of Saul's conversion (Acts 9:1-20) have been told using only declarative sentences? It probably could have, but sentences that ask questions are important also.

Interrogative sentences ask *questions.* They may request information, seek directions, or ask for explanations.

If the English language made no provision for asking questions, you might be able to express your desire for a *tangible* object by touching it or pointing to it and then to yourself. Asking for something not present or not visible would be much more difficult. Asking about something **abstract**, such as faith, religion, loyalty, or patriotism, would be impossible.

Interrogative sentences usually do not follow a simple subject-verb pattern. A question may begin with an interrogative pronoun: *who, which,* or *what.*

Example: Who left this chair in the aisle?

Interrogative sentences may also begin with adverbs, such as *what, where, when,* or *how.*

Example: How do you know?

Write six interrogative sentences. Begin each question with one of the interrogative pronouns or one of the preceding adverbs. Remember to capitalize and punctuate correctly.

1.26 _____

1.27 _____

1.28 _____

1.29 _____

1.30 _____

1.31 _____

Questions may also begin with **auxiliary** (or helping) **verbs**. Auxiliary verbs are used to express meanings that a single verb by itself could not express.

Learn to recognize these important auxiliary verbs:

shall	would	has	am
will	should	had	is
may	must	do	was
can	might	does	were
could	have	did	are

Examples: *Shall* I go with you?
Did you finish?
Is Sharon going with us?

Notice that in a question that begins with an auxiliary verb, the main verb and its helper are split or divided by a noun or a pronoun (the subject).

5

Rewrite these sentences. Change each statement to a question by introducing the sentence with the auxiliary verb. Divide the main verb and its helper with the correct noun or pronoun. Remember to punctuate correctly.

Example: Tom is going to the game.

_____Is Tom going to the game?_____

1.32   You have finished your report.

_____

1.33   Cats can climb trees.

_____

1.34   I must go to bed now.

_____

1.35   I may have a slice of pie.

_____

1.36   You can return your library book.

_____

Write five interrogative sentences. Begin each question with an auxiliary verb. Remember to punctuate correctly.

1.37   _____
1.38   _____
1.39   _____
1.40   _____
1.41   _____

Imperative sentences. An imperative sentence gives a command or an order or a very urgent request. Imperative sentences frequently do not have stated subjects. Rather, the subject is _implied,_ or understood.

Example: (_You_) Close the door.

Direct commands are often expressed by the simple form of the verb.

Example: Finish the test.

Negative commands are often expressed with _do not_ or the contraction _don't._

Example: _Do not_ go in the water.

Emphatic imperatives may be punctuated with an exclamation mark. Even though an exclamation point is used, the *function* is still imperative.

Example: Halt!

Attention!

Polite imperative sentences use adverbs of courtesy, such as *please,* or auxiliary verbs. Softened or polite imperatives may be punctuated with question marks. These sentences remain imperative in function.

Example: *Please* come here.
Will you erase the blackboard?

The function of the sentence, not the end punctuation, determines whether the sentence is imperative.

Write five imperative sentences. Use a variety of the patterns given in the preceding examples with the proper punctuation.

1.42   _____

1.43   _____

1.44   _____

1.45   _____

1.46   _____

Exclamatory sentences. Exclamatory sentences express strong feelings or emotions or emphatic statements of facts or opinion. An exclamation may be only one word, a phrase, or a fully developed sentence.

Examples: Oh!
At last!
How fortunate you are!

Notice that exclamatory sentences are punctuated with exclamation marks.

Can a single word or a phrase (as in the first two preceding examples) truly be considered a sentence? Even the experts do not always agree. Many experts say that even though the words lack the subject and predicate that traditionally characterize the sentence, the meaning is clear and independent. Therefore, such one-word imperatives or phrase imperatives and exclamations are considered to be sentences.

The occasional use of exclamatory sentences not only lends emphasis to ideas, but it also adds variety to a piece of writing. However, you should guard against scattering exclamation points throughout your writing just for the sake of variety. The use of too many exclamation marks actually *decreases* emphasis. Usually only an immature or inexperienced writer makes this mistake.

Write five exclamatory sentences. For this exercise, write fully developed sentences, not just single words or phrases.

Example: The house is on fire!

1.47 _____

1.48 _____

1.49 _____

1.50 _____

1.51 _____

Complete these statements.

1.52 A sentence that tells something about the subject is a _____ sentence.

1.53 An _____ sentence asks a question.

1.54 A sentence that expresses a command is an _____ sentence.

1.55 A sentence that expresses strong feeling is an _____ sentence.

1.56 Something that is capable of being touched is _____ .

1.57 Meanings that a single verb by itself could not express are expressed by _____ .

1.58 An exclamatory sentence is punctuated with an _____ .

1.59 An interrogative sentence is punctuated with a _____ .

1.60 A declarative sentence is punctuated with a _____ .

1.61 An imperative sentence is most often punctuated with a _____ .

Teacher check _____

Initial   Date

8

SENTENCE ERRORS

You have learned that a sentence is a group of words (1) that express a complete thought and (2) that are punctuated as an independent unit.

Notice that a sentence has two requirements. Both of these requirements must be met. You should develop a "sentence sense" so that you will be able to recognize a complete thought. You also should be able to tell the difference between one sentence (one complete thought) and two.

Test your "sentence sense" with the following activity.

 Complete this activity.

In the following thirteen sentences, proper nouns and all pronouns referring to Jesus are capitalized for you. Quotation marks and commas are provided for you. You will need to capitalize the first word of each sentence. You will need to supply the correct end punctuation. You will need to write the sentences in paragraphs.

1.62　　　　Jesus and His disciples were resting in the desert near the city of Bethsaida when the people learned where Jesus was, they followed Him Jesus received them He told them of the kingdom of God toward evening His disciples asked Jesus to send the people to get food Jesus answered, "Give ye them to eat" the disciples had only five loaves and two fishes "how can we feed five thousand people" they asked Jesus took the five loaves and the two fishes looking up to heaven, He blessed them then He broke the bread and divided the fishes every person had all he could eat after the meal, the disciples gathered up twelve baskets of food that remained

Faulty or incorrect sentences are called sentence errors. Three of the most common and most serious errors are *sentence fragments, comma-splice sentences,* and *run-on sentences.*

Sentence fragment. As you have learned, to be a sentence a group of words must state a complete thought and must make sense by itself.

If a group of words does not meet these two requirements, it may be a fragment or only a piece of a sentence. A sentence fragment is interrupted by a period before the thought is complete.

A fragment is a group of words, often a phrase or a clause, that is punctuated as a sentence but does not express a complete thought.

Example: That I built with scrap lumber Dad had given me.

Although the group of words above contains a noun (I) and a verb (built), the words do not state a complete thought. We do not know what was built. It may have been a doghouse, a sled, a boxcar racer, or something entirely different. The words cannot stand alone.

Everyone uses fragments of sentences in casual, informal conversation. Suppose someone asks you, "How old are you?" You will answer simply, "Thirteen."

In formal written English, however, fragmentary sentences are incorrect.

Complete the following exercise. Read the sentence fragments. They may be puzzling to you. Remember that lack of clarity is one reason fragmentary sentences are incorrect. Use your imagination. Rewrite each group, adding or subtracting words as necessary to make one or more complete sentences.

Example: That I made in art class

For Christmas I gave candlesticks that I made in art class.

1.63   I'm going to Montana. Probably next summer.

_____

1.64   I saw Tom after school. Out on the football field.

_____

1.65   That Mother forgot about and left in the oven too long.

_____
_____

1.66   Did you ever get hiccups? That just wouldn't quit?

_____

1.67   If that phone rings one more time!

_____

1.68   I have to get a signed permission slip. Before I can go on the field trip.

_____
_____

1.69   When the popcorn is ready.

_____

1.70   Trying to be fair. He is my friend, after all.

_____

_____

Comma-splice sentences.   Comma-splice sentences are two complete sentences that have been incorrectly joined by a comma.

To correct a comma-splice sentence, you have several choices. One of the complete sentences can be changed. It can be made less important so that it will no longer express a complete thought. To make an idea less important is to *subordinate* it.   The following example shows this method for correcting comma-splice sentences.

Comma-splice: The bakery was closed, we could not get the birthday cake.

You will probably agree that the birthday cake is the most important thought in the example comma-splice sentence. Therefore the other thought, *The bakery was closed,* can be turned into a less important part of the main sentence.

Rewritten: Since the bakery was closed, we could not get the birthday cake.

Sometimes both of the complete thoughts in a comma-splice sentence are equally important. The comma-splice sentence may be rewritten using a coordinating conjunction preceded by a comma. The coordinating conjunctions are *and, but, or,* and *nor.*

Comma-splice: This summer we will visit my grandmother, we can stay only two weeks.

Rewritten: This summer we will visit my grandmother, *but* we can only stay two weeks.

Another way to correct a comma-splice sentence is by substituting a semicolon for the comma if the main clauses are closely related.

Comma-splice: Buy that one, it looks nice on you.
Rewritten: Buy that one; it looks nice on you.

Perhaps the simplest way to correct a comma-splice sentence is to divide it into two or more complete sentences separated by a period.

Comma-splice: Our class helped raise money to buy new hymnals, next year we hope to give visual aids to the Sunday school.

The two complete thoughts contained in the preceding comma-splice sentence are of equal importance. However, if they are joined by a conjunction, the resulting sentence is too long to be effective. The best solution is to make two complete sentences.

Rewritten: Our class helped raise money to buy new hymnals. Next year we hope to give visual aids to the Sunday school.

Practice what you have learned in the following activities.

Correct the comma-splice sentences. Use a variety of the methods you have learned.

Example: He scored the winning point, everyone cheered.
Rewritten: When he scored the winning point, everyone cheered.
                                    or
                  He scored the winning point, and everyone cheered.
                                    or
                  He scored the winning point. Everyone cheered.

1.71   The days are warmer, it will soon be summer.

_____

1.72   Gerald cannot go hiking, his ankle is not healed.

_____

1.73   Cats are fine pets, if you like them, I would rather have a dog.

_____

1.74   I love to sing Christmas carols, I cannot always carry the tune.

_____

1.75   Do not plant the seeds too deep, they will not come up.

_____

1.76   Have you finished your book report, I have not even started mine yet.

_____

1.77   Sandy is bringing potato salad, Lee is bringing hot dogs, we will have a picnic in the park.

_____

_____

1.78   Tim helps his neighbors do yard work on Saturdays, he earns extra money that way.

_____

_____

Run-on sentences. Run-on sentences, sometimes called run-together sentences, make excessive use of the conjunctions *and* and *so* in joining several main clauses into one sentence.

Usually the best method for correcting run-on sentences is to subordinate one of the main clauses.

Run-on sentence:

> We went to town yesterday and we bought some school supplies and we ate a hamburger and we went home.

Rewritten:

> When we went to town yesterday, we bought school supplies, ate a hamburger, and went home.

If all of the ideas in the run-on sentence are equally important, you might divide the run-on into separate sentences.

Run-on sentence:

> Two cars crashed together at the Uniontown turn off and the county rescue unit quickly freed the men and miraculously the three men escaped unhurt.

Revised sentence:

> Two cars crashed together at the Uniontown turn off. The county rescue unit quickly freed the trapped men. Miraculously, the three men escaped unhurt.

Other methods for correcting the run-on sentence include making part of the sentence compound by joining two main clauses with a comma and a conjunction or by using a semicolon between two closely connected main clauses.

Run-on sentence:

> Two of my best friends live close to my house *and* we visit each other every afternoon after school and play catch.

Rewritten:

> Two of my best friends live close to my house; and we visit each other every afternoon after school and play catch.

Rewritten:

> Two of my best friends live close to my house, we visit each other every afternoon after school and play catch.

A combination of methods can also be used.

Run-on sentence:

> I did not know if Dad would let me go to the game *so* I stopped by his office after school *and* I asked him *and* he said I could, *so* I bought the tickets.

Revised sentence:

> Because I did not know if Dad would let me go to the game, I stopped by his office after school and asked him. When he said I could go, I bought the tickets.

Correct the run-on sentence in this paragraph.

1.79

The professor said that thousands of high school graduates could not pass the college entrance exams and were rejected and that most of their deficiencies could have been prevented by a proper education and this fact proved that public education was bad and that something ought to be done about it.

_____

_____

_____

_____

_____

_____

SPELLING

You have heard most of the following words and may have studied some of them before. Look them over carefully. If you are unsure of their pronunciation, use a dictionary or ask your teacher. Knowing how to pronounce and spell each word is as important as knowing what each word means.

Spelling Words -1		
classification	provision	pronunciation
structure	tangible	continue
function	abstract	describe
separate	opinion	believe
question	auxiliary	pattern
punctuation	introduction	excellent
persecute	command	frequent
vessel	exclamation	conquer
conversion	request	rhythm
sequence	quiet	lightning

List the six words containing the letter *q*.

1.80

a. _____ c. _____ e. _____

b. _____ d. _____ f. _____

List the ten spelling words that end in *-ion, -sion,* **or** *-tion.*

1.81

a. _____ f. _____

b. _____ g. _____

c. _____ h. _____

d. _____ i. _____

e. _____ j. _____

List the five spelling words that contain double letters.

1.82

a. _____

b. _____

c. _____

d. _____

e. _____

Ask your teacher to give you a practice spelling test of Spelling Words -1. Restudy the words you missed.

Teacher check _____

Initial   Date

Review the material in this section in preparation for the Self Test. The Self Test will check your mastery of this particular section. The items missed on this Self Test will indicate specific areas where restudy is needed for mastery.

SELF TEST 1

Match the term with the definition (each answer, 2 points).

1.01 _____ interrogative pronoun

1.02 _____ implied

1.03 _____ comma-splice sentence

1.04 _____ exclamation

1.05 _____ auxiliary verb

1.06 _____ coordinating conjunctions

1.07 _____ fragment

1.08 _____ imperative sentence

1.09 _____ declarative sentence

1.010 _____ sentence

a. group of words expressing a complete thought

b. makes a statement about the subject

c. asks a question

d. expresses a command

e. expresses strong feeling

f. *who, which,* or *what*

g. expresses meanings that a single verb by itself could not express

h. something that is not stated

i. adverbs of courtesy

j. negative command

k. words that are punctuated as a sentence but do not express a complete thought

l. two or more complete sentences joined by a comma

m. *and, but, for, or,* and *nor*

Complete these statements (each answer, 3 points).

1.011   Three of the most serious sentence errors are a. _____ ,
          b. _____ , and c. _____ .

1.012   The function of an imperative sentence is _____ .

1.013   The words *don't* or *do not* are often used to express a _____
          _____ .

1.014   Depending upon the tone, an imperative sentence can be punctuated
          with a(n) a. _____ , a(n) b. _____ ,
          or a(n) c. _____ .

1.015   Overuse of exclamation marks in written English _____
          _____ .

**Place the proper end punctuation on the line following each sentence and
write the sentence type according to function in the parentheses** (each answer,
2 points).

1.016   How many seashells did you find a. __ b. (_____)

1.017   Look out for that car a. __ b. (_____)

1.018   What a close call we had a. __ b. (_____)

1.019   The ink stain will not come out a. __ b. (_____)

1.020   Please help arrange the chairs a. __ b. (_____)

1.021   If I do not hurry, I will miss my bus a. __ b. (_____)

1.022   Would you close the window, please a. __ b. (_____)

1.023   Have you had your lunch a. __ b. (_____)

1.024   Fruit trees bordered the pasture a. __ b. (_____)

1.025   Do not stand up in the boat a. __ b. (_____)

Identify the correct sentences and the sentence errors. In the parentheses write
complete, run-on, fragment, or *comma-splice* (each answer, 3 points).

1.026   Finally we were all ready to board the plane. (_____)

1.027   After we took down the tent. (_____)

1.028   Does snow often fall where you live? (_____)

1.029   Even though the paint does not look wet. (_____)

1.030   A strong wind came up and the boats broke loose from the dock and they
          drifted away. (_____)

1.031   If you can hit a line drive. (_____)

1.032   Did you leave the porch light on, we will not be home until late tonight.
          (_____)

1.033   What Bible verse did you memorize? (_____)

1.034   I cannot see to study and it is too dark in here. (_____)

1.035   Because the runner was out of bounds. (_____)

Correct the sentence errors. Choose any five of the sentence errors (1.026-1.035). Rewrite each one, correcting the error (each answer, 5 points).

1.036 _____

_____

1.037 _____

_____

1.038 _____

_____

1.039 _____

_____

1.040 _____

_____

114 / 142

Score _____

Teacher check _____

Initial   Date

 Take your spelling test of Spelling Words-1.

II. WRITING PARAGRAPHS

In Section One you learned about four basic types of sentences. Now you will learn how a variety of sentences may be combined to form paragraphs.

Paragraphs perform several functions in the written English language. They break up a page of printing or writing and make it more readable. Paragraphs serve to focus the reader's attention on a single, central idea. Paragraphs may tell stories, impart information, persuade belief, or describe feelings. Effective written communication depends upon well-constructed paragraphs.

Most paragraphs in formal writing have topic sentences. In this section you will learn to recognize topic sentences and you will be able to practice writing topic sentences.

All of the other sentences in a paragraph should relate to the topic sentence. After you have learned to write topic sentences, you will have the opportunity to write simple paragraphs.

A paragraph is usually a part of a longer piece of writing. When you are able to write good paragraphs, you can write a lively personal letter, an interesting book report, or an informative research paper. You will find it easier to arrange and present facts when you must give an essay answer for an examination. If you are called upon to give your Christian witness in written form, good paragraph writing skills will make your message more effective.

You will become familiar with several terms that are important to the study of our written language. You will learn to identify, to spell, and to recognize terms relating to paragraphs.

SECTION OBJECTIVES

Review these objectives. When you have completed this section, you should be able to:

5. Spell new words.
6. Identify and explain inductive, deductive, and transitional paragraphs.
7. Explain and identify sequence and unity.

VOCABULARY

Study these words to enhance your learning success in this section.

anecdote (an' ik dōt). Short account of some interesting incident.

bow (bou). Forward part of a ship.

chronological (kron' u loj' u kul). Arranged according to sequence or order in time.

deductive (di duk' tiv). Reasoning from the general to the particular.

flaw (flô). A defect or a fault.

helm (helm). Steering wheel of a ship.

inductive (in duk' tiv). Reasoning from the particular to the general.

irrelevant (i rel' u vunt). Not to the point; off the subject.

keel (kēl). Main timber that runs the whole length of a ship's bottom.

luff (luf). Weather side of a ship.

sequence (sē' kwens). The coming of one thing after another in some order.

summation (su mā'shun). Final presentation of facts.

transition (tran zish'un). Passage linking one section of a composition with another.

PARAGRAPH COMPONENTS

A *paragraph* is a piece of writing that deals with one central idea or that gives the words of one speaker. A paragraph may consist of one or more sentences.

An *indention* signals the beginning of each new paragraph. To indent means to set the first sentence five or more spaces in from the left margin.

The sentence that states the main idea of a paragraph is called the *topic sentence.* A good topic sentence may be a *definition.* Often a topic sentence tells *time, place,* or *attitude.* The topic sentence is most frequently the first sentence of the paragraph. However, the topic sentence may appear within the paragraph or even as the last sentence of the paragraph. Sometimes the last sentence merely rephrases or reinforces the topic sentence.

When all the sentences in the paragraph support the topic sentence, the paragraph has unity. Unity results when the writer stays with one main idea from the beginning of the paragraph to the end, when all the sentences support the topic sentence.

In addition to supporting the topic sentence, the other sentences should be presented in some logical order, such as time or relative importance. **Sequence** is one name for the logical progression of facts or ideas.

Complete these statements.

2.1 Sentences that deal with a single idea or that give the words of a single speaker form a _____ .

2.2 The sentence that states the central idea of a paragraph is the _____ _____ .

2.3 A paragraph has _____ when all the sentences support the topic sentence.

2.4 When all the sentences of a paragraph are presented in logical order, that order is sometimes called _____ .

2.5 To set the first word five or more spaces in from the left margin is to _____ .

Read the following sentences and complete the activities.

When the time came to go home I could not open my locker. In my last period gym class I hurt my ankle. Today was a day when everything seemed to go wrong. Tomorrow I promise myself I will wake up on time. First I overslept. Then I realized I had forgotten my library book. My hobby is stamp collecting. Because of that, I almost missed my bus.

2.6 Do the preceding sentences combine to form a good paragraph? _____

2.7 Is the first sentence a good topic sentence? _____

2.8 Do all of the sentences relate to a single idea? _____

2.9 Are the sentences presented in a logical time sequence? _____

Read the sentences again and complete these activities.

2.10 The topic sentence is _____ _____ .

2.11 Rearrange the remaining sentences in a logical time sequence. To preserve unity, omit the sentence that does not support the topic sentence.

a. _____ _____

b. _____ _____

c. _____ _____

d. _____ _____

e. _____
_____

f. _____

g. The sentence that does not belong in the paragraph is _____
_____ .

Topic sentences. You have already learned that the topic sentence is the one which states the central idea of a paragraph. Often the topic sentence introduces a paragraph. When this condition is the case, all sentences in the paragraph should explain, reinforce, or support the topic sentence.

Sometimes the last sentence is the topic sentence. When the topic sentence concludes the paragraph, the topic sentence often serves as a summary or a climax. All of the other sentences lead up to the main idea as expressed in the topic sentence.

Occasionally the topic sentence occurs in the middle of the paragraph. The topic sentence tends to link, or to connect, the sentences that precede and follow it. The entire paragraph may be a **transition** paragraph.

You should be aware that not all paragraphs contain topic sentences. Sometimes the central idea of a paragraph in not expressed in a single sentence. It is only implied.

Topic sentences most often occur in *formal* written communication. Novels, magazine stories, and newspaper articles are examples of less formal writing. If you will examine a favorite book or story, you will notice that not every paragraph has a topic sentence. You may, however, find a paragraph such as the following one.

I had never seen the squire so near at hand. He was a tall man, over six feet high, and broad in proportion, and he had a bluff, rough-and-ready face, all roughened and reddened and lined in his long travels. His eyebrows were very black, and moved readily, and this gave him a look of some temper, not bad, you would say, but quick and high.

— *Treasure Island*, by Robert Louis Stevenson

In the preceding example paragraph the author describes Squire Trelawney as seen through the eyes of young Jim Hawkins.

When you read a well-constructed paragraph such as the example from *Treasure Island,* you are not aware of details such as topic sentences, unity, or sequence. You simply know that you enjoy reading the paragraph and you are eager to read more. Now you can better understand why skill in writing paragraphs is essential to effective communication.

Because a well-written topic sentence is the first step toward a well-written paragraph in formal writing, you will want to practice to develop your skill.

Remember that a good topic sentence may be a *definition*. The sentence may state a *fact* or an *opinion* or may ask a *question*. Often a topic sentence tells *time* or *place* or the writer's *attitude* or *feeling*.

You should not begin with such expressions as, "I am going to tell you about..." or "The book I read is about..." or "This is a paragraph about..."

Suppose you are a "shutter-bug" and you want to write about some aspects of your hobby of photography. You will not want to begin by writing, "This paragraph is going to be about photography."

The sentence states the central idea of the paragraph, but it is a sentence that belongs in your *thinking* process before you ever pick up your pen to write.

Once you have decided on your topic (in this example, some aspect of photography) you might write any one of the following topic sentences:

Topic sentences:

A camera is a box that has a lens to let in the light. (Definition)

A few simple rules will help you to take better photographs. (Fact)

I think color pictures are more fun to take than black and white ones. (Opinion)

Do you have a shoebox full of old family photographs somewhere around the house? (Question)

Last summer at Yellowstone National Park my brother and I took many pictures. (Time and place)

I enjoy taking unposed snapshots of my family. (Attitude or feeling)

 **Place a + in front of those sentences that you think are good topic sentences. Place a - before the ones that you believe do not meet the requirements for a good topic sentence. In the blank following each *good* topic sentence, place the proper descriptive term.**

Example: _+_ Psalm 8 is one of my favorite Psalms. (Attitude or feeling)

2.12 _____ The book I am going to tell about is *The Little Shepherd of Kingdom Come.* _____

2.13 _____ Tulip bulbs have an unusual history. _____

2.14 _____ I always look forward to vacation Bible school. _____

2.15 _____ This paragraph is about my city government. _____

2.16 _____ Nitrogen is a colorless, odorless gas. _____

2.17 _____ I think daily Bible reading is important for all Christians.

_____

2.18 _____ Sunday afternoons at my home are special family times.

_____

2.19 _____ A hymn is a song of praise to God. _____

2.20 _____ Have you accepted Jesus Christ as your personal Savior?

_____

Write six good topic sentences. Try to use each of the types you have studied in this section.

2.21   (Definition) _____

_____

_____

2.22   (Fact) _____

_____

2.23   (Opinion) _____

_____

2.24   (Time and place) _____

_____

2.25   (Attitude or feeling) _____

_____

_____

2.26   (Question) _____

_____

_____

Complete these statements.

2.27   A topic sentence states the _____ of the paragraph.

2.28   A topic sentence most often occurs in _____ writing.

2.29   When the topic sentence is missing, the central idea of the paragraph may be _____ .

Unity. A good paragraph sticks to the point. A paragraph that contains unrelated sentences loses its effect. As a result, the reader may become confused or even misled. When the writer stays with one main idea from the beginning of the paragraph to the end, that paragraph has *unity*.

Study the following paragraph and complete the activities.

We feed wild birds in the winter. I love winter, even when it snows. My brother, Mark, has promised to let me use his snowsled next winter. Of course, one bad thing is having to bundle up in so many heavy sweaters, but we can have a roaring fire in the fireplace.

2.30   Do you think the group of sentences above form a well written paragraph? _____

2.31   Is a topic sentence clearly stated? _____

2.32   Do all of the sentences relate directly to a topic sentence? _____

Your answer to all three questions is probably *no*.

The example sentences do not comprise a good paragraph in written English, although we might speak similar sentences in a casual, informal conversation.

Although the sentences are all loosely connected to wintertime, they do not relate directly to a single topic or central idea. In fact, almost any one of the sentences could be rewritten in the form of a topic sentence. In that case the remaining sentences could not simply be rearranged. They would have to be rewritten as well.

Read the paragraph and complete the activities.

> Each winter we feed the wild birds. Many of the birds come to our feeder from colder parts of the country. We put out crumbs, seeds, suet, and sometimes bits of fruit. The feeder tray is right outside our window. We enjoy watching the birds while they eat.

2.33   Which sentence is the topic sentence? _____

_____

2.34   Do all the sentences relate directly to the topic sentence? _____

2.35   Does the paragraph have unity? _____

2.36   Can you find any sentences that do not belong in the paragraph? _____

2.37   How many words can you find in the paragraph that reinforce the idea of *feeding* wild birds? List them.

a. _____   e. _____

b. _____   f. _____

c. _____   g. _____

d. _____   h. _____

Think before you write!

You will soon be ready to practice what you have learned about paragraphs to this point. The following tips will help you to succeed.

Think before you write.

The first *writing* step is the topic sentence, but the first *thinking* step is to select your topic and to have in mind what you want to say about it.

Next you will need to know the details you want to include. You may make a mental list, or you may jot down your ideas on scratch paper.

The third step is to plan how you intend to connect or relate the details you will use. Keep similar or related information together. Do not include anything **irrelevant**. Do not hesitate to repeat some specific terms or carefully chosen synonyms. Use connecting words to show how statements relate to each other in your paragraph. These connecting words will help the reader to follow your written thoughts.

If you wish, you may turn back to Activities 2.11 and 2.12. Notice such words as *today, because of that, first, then, when the time came, in my last period,* and *tomorrow.* These words help to relate the sentences in a logical order.

Other connecting words that will help you are *some, others, one important reason, still more, next, after that, therefore,* and *as a result.* You will be able to think of many more. Remember, you do not have to start every sentence with connecting words.

The following examples may help you choose a topic:

- A favorite Psalm
- A favorite Bible character
- A hobby
- A book you have enjoyed
- A sport

- A funny incident
- A historic marker near your home
- An unusual pet
- A science experiment
- Importance of daily prayer

Suppose you select a favorite Bible character as your topic. Then you must write your topic sentence. Some sentences you might write about this topic include the following examples:

My favorite Bible character is Paul.

or

On the road to Damascus, Paul was converted.

or

Paul was commissioned to carry the Gospel to the Gentiles.

If you choose a statement similar to the first one, all your supporting sentences should explain *why* Paul is your favorite.

If you choose the second statement, all your supporting sentences should describe Paul's *conversion.*

With the third example you may choose to describe Paul's special *commission* as told in Acts 16:13–20, or you may tell about his *missions* to Asia Minor, Greece, and Rome.

The supporting details you will include depend entirely upon your topic sentence.

Write a paragraph. Remember to think before you write. Select your topic. You may use some of the suggestions in this section or a topic of your own choice. Plan what you want to say. Begin with a topic sentence. Write three or four sentences which directly relate to or support your topic sentence.

2.38

_____
_____
_____
_____
_____
_____
_____
_____

Teacher check _____
                               Initial   Date

Sequence. In Language Arts LIFEPAC 703 you studied _sequence of events_ in reading, understanding, and enjoying biographies. Now you are about to learn the importance of a logical order of events and ideas, or sequence, in writing well-constructed paragraphs.

To be most effective, the sentences in your paragraph that support the topic sentence should be presented in some logical order. To a certain extent the order you choose will depend upon the ideas or facts you wish to present.

Order of _chronology_ is one common sequence. **Chronological**, or time, order simply means that events are presented in the order in which they occurred: first, second, third, and so on. You would usually tell an **anecdote** in chronological order.

Order of _importance_ is another method of presenting facts. You may wish to state the most important item first, the second most important item next, and the third most important item last. However, you should remember that the reverse order—leading up to the most important statement—is often more effective.

Order of _complexity_ is yet another possible way to organize facts or ideas in a logical manner. Usually this sequence begins with material that is easily understood and gradually progresses to more and more difficult concepts.

 Read the following paragraph and complete the activities.

Paul was known as the "Apostle to the Gentiles." First he went to Antioch and worked for a year among the Gentiles. In Antioch he worked with a church whose members were the first to be called Christians. Later Paul was sent by the Antioch church on three important missions to non-Jewish people of Asia Minor, Greece, and Rome.

2.39   Change the topic sentence to a question beginning with the word *why*.

_____

2.40   Do all of the sentences in the paragraph help to answer the question? (This question is one way to check for unity.) _____

2.41   What logical order of presentation, or *sequence*, is used? (Notice such words as *first* and *later*.) _____

2.42   Does the repetition of certain words or their synonyms help to relate all the sentences to the central idea? _____

LANGUAGE ARTS

ARTS 7 0 9

LIFEPAC TEST

71 / 89

Name _____

Date _____

Score _____

LANGUAGE ARTS 709: LIFEPAC TEST

Match the following words or terms with the definition (each answer, 2 points).

1. _____ implied
2. _____ topic sentence
3. _____ sequence
4. _____ comma splice
5. _____ alliterative
6. _____ pronunciation
7. _____ chronological
8. _____ limerick
9. _____ pseudonym
10. _____ anonymous

a. an author's pen name
b. having first letters or sounds alike
c. sentence that states central idea of paragraph
d. letters that occur in spelling that are not pronounced
e. involves sounds made and syllables accented
f. speaking clearly and distinctly in forming sounds
g. words that are adopted from other languages
h. form of humorous verse, usually five lines
i. two or more sentences joined by a comma
j. suggested, not stated
k. logical progression of facts or ideas
l. in order of time or occurrence
m. in order of complexity
n. to convince or persuade
o. author's name is unknown or not given

Answer *true* **or** *false* (each answer, 1 point).

11. _____ In the English language each letter of the alphabet has only one sound.
12. _____ When you read aloud from the Bible, you should be able to pronounce all of the words correctly.
13. _____ When you read silently, whether you can pronounce the words correctly does not matter.
14. _____ Edward Lear's name is often associated with the limerick.
15. _____ "Tongue twisters" are not only fun, but they are also a helpful aid to correct pronunciation.
16. _____ "Nonsense" literature is especially associated with the English language.
17. _____ The same word will be pronounced the same way, regardless of its meaning or part of speech.
18. _____ Adding many irrelevant facts to a paragraph makes it more interesting.
19. _____ A word that is commonly mispronounced is frequently misspelled as well.
20. _____ Scattering exclamation marks through your writing makes it more exciting.

1

Write the letter that explains each term (each answer, 2 points).

21. _____ fragment
    a. a vessel
    b. period
    c. incomplete
    d. ship's sail

22. _____ function
    a. purpose
    b. fictitious
    c. connection
    d. punctuation

23. _____ interrogation
    a. statement
    b. command
    c. request
    d. question

24. _____ auxiliary
    a. helping
    b. barring the way
    c. continued
    d. negative

25. _____ climax
    a. beginning part
    b. middle part
    c. highest point
    d. transition point

26. _____ anecdote
    a. short, lively story
    b. space from left margin
    c. off the subject
    d. diacritical mark

27. _____ persuade
    a. type of cloth
    b. win over to belief
    c. pertaining to sound
    d. aid to pronunciation

28. _____ flaw

a. logical order

b. tongue exercises

c. fault or defect

d. abstract

29. _____ irrelevant

a. change of scene

b. not to the point

c. exciting details

d. command or request

30. _____ coined

a. emphasized

b. repaired

c. invented

d. polished

Complete these statements by writing the best word or term in the space provided (each answer, 3 points).

31. The pseudonym of Charles L. Dodgson is _____ .

32. An imperative sentence may be punctuated by a(n) a. _____ ,
    b. _____ , or c. _____ .

33. The topic sentence is usually the first sentence in a _____
    paragraph.

34. A form of humorous verse, probably named after a city in Ireland, is the
    _____ .

35. Lines that repeat the same first letter or sound are _____ .

36. Lines that have the same ending sounds _____ .

37. Lines with a strong beat or accent have _____ .

38. When the author's name is not known or given, the written item is
    _____ .

39. The most serious and most common sentence errors are a. _____ ,
    b. _____ , and c. _____ .

Take your LIFEPAC Spelling Test.

3

Complete these activities.

2.43 Write another paragraph. Write a topic sentence. Write four or five sentences that explain or support the central idea expressed in your topic sentence. If you can, use a variety of the four sentence types you studied in this section. As you work, check for unity in your supporting sentences. Repeat some words or use carefully chosen synonyms to help insure unity. Be sure that your facts or ideas are presented in some logical sequence. Make liberal use of the connecting words you have learned.

_____

_____

_____

_____

_____

_____

_____

_____

_____

_____

Complete this self-check:

☐ Do I have a good topic sentence?
☐ Have I used a variety of sentence types?
☐ Do all my sentences relate directly to the central idea?
☐ Have I repeated certain words and ideas for emphasis?
☐ Have I included any sentences that do not belong in this paragraph?
☐ Is all my information presented in a logical order?
☐ Have I made use of connecting words to help guide the reader?

After you have checked over your own paragraph very carefully, your teacher or assistant will want to read it also. Your teacher may ask you to read your paragraph aloud to the class. If so, ask your fellow students to apply the check list to your paragraph and be prepared to do the same for them.

Teacher check _____

Initial   Date

PARAGRAPH PATTERNS

The placement of the topic sentence within a paragraph determines the paragraph pattern. The two basic paragraph patterns are the **deductive** pattern and the **inductive** pattern. A third pattern might be called _transitional_.

In a deductive paragraph the topic sentence is usually the first sentence. All other sentences in the paragraph explain or support the topic sentence.

In an inductive paragraph the topic sentence is the last sentence. All the other sentences lead up to the topic sentence. The topic sentence serves as the conclusion or climax of the paragraph or as a summary or tying together of all the details contained in the paragraph.

If the topic sentence comes somewhere in the middle of the paragraph, the topic sentence links or connects the sentences that precede and follow it. It provides a transition.

Deductive paragraphs. Remember that in a deductive paragraph the topic sentence is the first sentence, and all other sentences relate to the central idea. The paragraph from *Treasure Island* that appears earlier in this section is an example of a deductive paragraph. The paragraphs you have written so far in this section have been deductive paragraphs.

Complete this activity.

2.44 Read Job 1:1–5 and use the information you are given to write a deductive paragraph. The topic sentence is supplied for you. Read the passage from the Scriptures. Then, in your mind or on a piece of scratch paper, make a list of four or five statements you can make about Job.
Remember that each sentence should relate directly to the topic sentence. Then write the paragraph.

A man lived in the land of Uz, whose name was Job. _____

_____

_____

_____

_____

_____

_____

_____

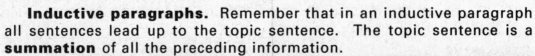

Teacher check _____

                           Initial   Date

Inductive paragraphs. Remember that in an inductive paragraph all sentences lead up to the topic sentence. The topic sentence is a **summation** of all the preceding information.

The following paragraph, also from *Treasure Island,* is an example of an inductive paragraph.

> On our little walk along the quays, he made himself the most interesting companion, telling me about the different ships that we passed by, their rig, tonnage, and nationality, explaining the work that was going forward—how one was discharging, another taking in cargo, and a third making ready for sea; and every now and then telling me some little anecdote of ships or seamen, or repeating a nautical phrase till I had learned it perfectly. I began to see that here was one of the best possible shipmates.
>
> —*Treasure Island*, by Robert Louis Stevenson

When your purpose is to *convince* or to *persuade* your reader, you may wish to present your details, facts, or opinions first. Then you will tie all these together in your final statement. A paragraph written in this pattern is an inductive paragraph.

Many examples of inductive paragraphs appear in the Bible, particularly in the New Testament. Perhaps the Bible was written in this way because inductive paragraphs make teaching and learning more effective.

Complete this activity.

2.45 Read Matthew 6:28–30.
   a. Do these verses fulfill the requirements of an inductive paragraph?
   _____

   b. Notice that the first sentence asks a question. Do the other sentences lead up to the summation or conclusion presented in the last verse?
   _____

   Perhaps you can find other Biblical examples of inductive paragraphs to share with your class.

   Remember, even though the topic sentence concludes the paragraph instead of introducing it, the inductive paragraph calls for the same unity and sequence required of all paragraphs.

Read the following paragraph and complete the activities.

When my brother Mark brought home a baby raccoon he found in the woods, we thought at first it would be a perfect family pet. We named him Tubby because he was so round and plump. Dad helped us build a box for him to sleep in. Mother found some soft, clean rags for his bed. We laughed and laughed as we watched Tubby eat and play. As Tubby grew bigger and stronger, our laughter stopped. Tubby scattered Dad's neckties all over the house. He broke Mom's favorite cookie jar. He

knocked over Mark's bike. He treed our cat. He even chewed up all the rolled newspapers I had ready for my paper route. Finally Dad had to call the Game Warden to come get Tubby and to return him to the woods where he belonged. We were sad to see him go, but we had learned a valuable lesson. Wild animals do not always make good pets.

2.46   The first sentence tells you that the paragraph will be about a baby raccoon that became a family pet. What is the topic sentence?

a. _____

_____

Do all sentences provide supporting details? b. _____

Does the topic sentence provide a summary or conclusion? c. _____

2.47   How many sentences does the paragraph contain? a. _____

This paragraph is one of the longest ones we have studied in this section. Do you think this paragraph could be expanded to a theme of several paragraphs' length? b. _____

2.48   In the first sentence, the words, *we thought at first,* give you a hint about the ending. What sentence near the middle of the paragraph provides a strong clue that Tubby leaves much to be desired as an ideal family pet?

_____

_____

Notice how these words help to lead up to, and to prepare the reader for, the final conclusion.

2.49   List several connecting words from the paragraph about Tubby that help to establish sequence.

a. _____   c. _____

b. _____   d. _____

The first step in writing an inductive paragraph is to decide upon your topic sentence, even though the topic sentence will appear last in the paragraph. It may help you in your thinking process to say to yourself: "Therefore I believe..." or "For these reasons I think...." These words need not necessarily appear in your written paragraph. The following examples of topic sentences are to help you start your thinking.

Daily Bible reading helps me grow spiritually.

A well balanced breakfast is a good way to start the day.

"Cramming" the night before an examination can have unfortunate results.

The care you give your horse after exercise is as important as exercise itself.

You never know when something you do or say can lead someone else to Christ.

I know that prayers are answered.

Write a paragraph.

2.50   On a separate sheet of paper write an inductive paragraph.

Transitional paragraph. In a longer piece of writing, a paragraph with the topic sentence in the middle frequently serves as a transitional paragraph. *Transition* means a change. In fiction the transition may be a change of season, setting, character, or action. The following example is a transitional paragraph with the topic sentence in the middle.

The *Hispaniola* lay some way out, and we went under the figureheads and round the sterns of many other ships, and their cables sometimes grated underneath our **keel**, and sometimes swung above us. At last, however, we got alongside, and were met and saluted as we stepped aboard by the mate, Mr. Arrow, a brown old sailor, with earrings in his ears and a squint. He and the squire were very thick and friendly, but I soon observed that things were not the same between Mr. Trelawney and the captain.

—*Treasure Island*, by Robert Louis Stevenson

The sentence which begins, "At last, however, we got alongside..." is the topic sentence that links the sentences which precede and follow it. In addition, the entire paragraph serves as a transition, or change, from the Admiral Benbow Inn to the ship.

You have already learned that not every paragraph has a topic sentence. This fact is especially true in novels, short stories, magazine articles, and newspaper articles.

However, even if the topic sentence is only implied or suggested, the paragraph still should be limited to one central idea or the thoughts or words of only one person. The following selection is an example of a paragraph without a topic sentence.

Now, just after sundown, when all my work was over, and I was on my way to me berth, it occurred to me that I should like an apple. I ran on deck. The watch was all forward looking out for the island. The man at the **helm** was watching the **luff** of the sail, and whistling away gently to himself; and that was the only sound excepting the swish of the sea against the **bows** and around the sides of the ship.

—*Treasure Island,* by Robert Louis Stevenson

The paragraph has no topic sentence. The central idea of the paragraph is not really Jim Hawkins' sudden desire to munch on a crisp, juicy apple. If you will read the paragraph closely, you will realize that it has both unity and sequence. In the story the paragraph is the author's way of having Jim Hawkins hide in the apple barrel, where he will overhear a sinister conversation.

Complete this activity.

2.51 Find an example of a transitional paragraph or a paragraph having no topic sentence. Share your example with a friend.

Teacher check _____

                    Initial   Date

PARAGRAPH FLAWS

A poorly written paragraph is difficult to read and difficult to understand. A poor paragraph lacks a topic sentence or fails to stick closely to one central idea. The sentences in a poorly constructed paragraph do not all explain or support the topic sentence or the central idea. Including irrelevant details weakens a paragraph and may confuse or mislead the reader.

Although a paragraph may consist of only one sentence, paragraphs should not be too short and choppy. On the other hand, a paragraph that is too long may cause the reader to lose interest.

Absence of central idea. Even if it has no stated topic sentence, each paragraph should have one main or central idea. The absence of a central idea is a serious **flaw**.

Absence of supporting details. Most paragraphs will contain at least two or three sentences. All of them should support the topic sentence or central idea. The absence of supporting details weakens a paragraph and fails to inform or to convince the reader. The paragraph that lacks supporting details does not effectively communicate the central idea.

Write a paragraph on a separate sheet of paper and complete the following self-check questions. Choose a topic or ask your teacher for suggestions.

2.52   Make this paragraph longer than your previous ones. After you have finished, complete the self-check questions. If necessary, revise and rewrite your paragraph.
Self-Check Questions

2.53   What is your topic sentence? _____
_____
_____

2.54   If you have chosen to write a paragraph without a stated topic, what is your central idea? _____
_____

2.55   What paragraph pattern have you used? _____

2.56   How many sentences have you used? _____

2.57   Have you used a variety of sentence types? _____

2.58   Do all your sentences relate directly to the topic sentence or central idea?
_____

2.59   Can you find any sentence that does not belong in your paragraph?
_____

2.60   List some of the words and synonyms you have repeated in order to assure unity.

a. _____ d. _____ g. _____
b. _____ e. _____ h. _____
c. _____ f. _____ i. _____

2.61   In what order have you presented your ideas of facts? _____

2.62   List some of the connecting words you have used in your paragraph to insure sequence.

a. _____ d. _____ g. _____
b. _____ e. _____ h. _____
c. _____ f. _____ i. _____

2.63   Have you checked the correct spelling of words if you are uncertain?
_____

2.64   Have you tried to make your paragraph interesting? _____

Teacher check _____
                              Initial   Date

2.65   Copy your revised paragraph on a separate piece of paper. Try to use
        your neatest handwriting.

Teacher check _____

                        Initial   Date

SPELLING

The words in Spelling Words-2 have the suffix *-tion* or *-tive*. Learning to
spell these words correctly will help you study and will add to your reading
comprehension.

--- Spelling Words -2 ---

indention	devotion	inductive
transition	promotion	creative
summation	communication	instructive
repetition	creation	relative
composition	confirmation	legislative
definition	resolution	cumulative
preposition	salvation	native
tradition	deductive	meditative

Complete these sentences.

2.66   The *-tion* words are all _____ (part of speech).
2.67   The *-tive* words are all _____ (part of speech).

**Change the following nouns to adjectives by changing the suffix
from** *-tion* **to** *-tive*.

        Example: creation _____ creative _____
2.68   transition   _____
2.69   repetition   _____
2.70   definition   _____
2.71   promotion   _____
2.72   communication   _____

**Change the following adjectives to nouns by changing the suffix
from** *-tive* **to** *-tion.*

        Example: cumulative _____ cumulation _____
2.73   deductive   _____
2.74   inductive   _____
2.75   creative   _____
2.76   instructive   _____

2.77	relative	_____
2.78	legislative	_____
2.79	native	_____
2.80	meditative	_____

Place the proper infinitives on the lines.

Example: promotion _____to promote_____

2.81	indention	_____
2.82	summation	_____
2.83	composition	_____
2.84	confirmation	_____
2.85	resolution	_____
2.86	salvation	_____

Ask your teacher to give you a practice spelling test of Spelling Words-2. Restudy the words you missed.

Review the material in this section in preparation for the Self Test. This Self Test will check your mastery of this particular section as well as your knowledge of the previous section.

SELF TEST 2

Answer *true* **or** *false* (each answer, 1 point).

2.01	_____	All paragraphs must have a topic sentence.
2.02	_____	All paragraphs should contain one central idea or the words of one speaker.
2.03	_____	A paragraph must contain at least five sentences.
2.04	_____	The sentences in a paragraph should support the topic sentence or central idea.
2.05	_____	The facts or opinions in a paragraph should be presented in some logical order or sequence.
2.06	_____	Something that is tangible may be pointed to or touched.
2.07	_____	Imperative sentences may be punctuated with periods, exclamation marks, or question marks.
2.08	_____	A coordinating conjunction preceded by a comma can be used to correct a run-on sentence.
2.09	_____	The end punctuation determines sentence function.
2.010	_____	The sentence is a basic unit of written English communication.

Match these terms with the correct definition (each answer, 2 points).

2.011 _____ irrelevant

2.012 _____ fragment

2.013 _____ sentence errors

2.014 _____ question mark

2.015 _____ flaw

2.016 _____ indent

2.017 _____ "sentence sense"

2.018 _____ persuade

2.019 _____ comma splice

2.020 _____ anecdote

2.021 _____ precede

2.022 _____ summation

2.023 _____ implied

2.024 _____ sequence

2.025 _____ interrogative sentence

2.026 _____ conclusion

a. to set five or more spaces from the left margin

b. a brief story of an interesting incident

c. to win over to a belief

d. having nothing to do with the subject

e. to go before in rank or importance

f. final decision or last argument

g. suggested, not stated

h. brief statement of main points

i. an imperfection

j. a logical order

k. only a part of a sentence

l. ability to recognize a complete thought in sentence form

m. faulty or incorrect sentences

n. end punctuation of an interrogative sentence

o. an abstract idea, such as faith or loyalty

p. interrogative pronouns

q. sentence that asks a question

r. two sentences joined with a comma

Define or explain the following words or terms (each answer, 4 points).

2.027 deductive paragraph _____

_____

2.028 inductive paragraph _____

_____

2.029 auxiliary verb _____

_____

2.030 comma-splice error _____

_____

_____

2.031   transition _____

_____

_____

2.032   run-on sentence _____

_____

_____

2.033   chronological order _____

_____

_____

Complete these statements (each answer, 3 points).

2.034   A piece of writing that deals with one central idea is a _____ .

2.035   The beginning of each new paragraph is signaled by an _____ .

2.036   When the writer stays with one main idea from the beginning of the paragraph to the end, his paragraph should have _____ .

2.037   The logical progression of facts or information is called _____ .

2.038   To show a change of season, setting, character, or action a writer often uses a _____ paragraph.

2.039   If the central idea of a paragraph is not stated in a single sentence, it may be only _____ .

2.040   When the topic sentence ends the paragraph, the topic sentence often serves as a _____ .

2.041   When easily understood material appears first and gradually progresses to more and more difficult concepts, the paragraph is said to be in order of _____ .

2.042   The placement of the _____ within a paragraph determines the paragraph pattern.

2.043   Paragraphs least likely to have topic sentences are those in _____ _____ .

80 / 100

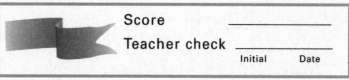

Score _____

Teacher check _____

Initial   Date

Take your spelling test of Spelling Words-2.

III. PRONOUNCING WORDS

If you are a good reader, you may have a large vocabulary of words that you recognize and understand when you see them in print. If you are a good student, you have worked hard to learn to spell certain words correctly and to use them effectively in written form.

By far the majority of our daily communication with other people is spoken. We communicate most often simply by speaking to one another.

Think for a moment. What was the very first thing you did this morning? You probably did not read a book or write a theme or take part in a spelling bee. You probably spoke. In fact, a verbal command may have awakened you.

You may have talked as you dressed, as you ate breakfast, as you were on your way to school, and as you greeted your teacher and your fellow students.

Because most of us speak more often than we read or write, effective spoken communication is every bit as important as other forms. Furthermore, the quality of your spoken English is often one way others may form their opinions of you. At home, in school, at church, in a social situation, or on a job, the way you speak can tell others whether you are an educated, Christian person.

Since we live in a democracy, we like to believe that *what* a person has to say is important, and not *how* he says it. In everyday life, however, this practice is seldom true.

Suppose you are explaining to someone that Jesus Christ is the center of your life. The words you choose to express yourself may be simple or profound. Although you may speak from a firm foundation of faith, incorrect English may prevent you from effective communication.

Speaking words correctly depends upon two things: **articulation** and **pronunciation**. Articulation involves speaking clearly and distinctly in forming and joining vowel and consonant sounds. Pronunciation involves the sounds made and the syllables accented. Pronunciation and articulation are so closely related that to separate them is sometimes difficult.

In this section you will learn to use a dictionary to determine the correct pronunciation of unfamiliar words. You will also learn a group of words that are often misspelled because they are often mispronounced. Correct pronunciation is often a step toward correct spelling.

You will learn about an unusual form of literature that is known as **"nonsense" verse**. You will have an opportunity to demonstrate articulation and pronunciation by reading aloud word lists and selections from "nonsense" literature.

SECTION OBJECTIVES

Review these objectives. When you have completed this section, you should be able to:

5. Spell new words.
8. Explain certain dictionary and pronunciation facts.
9. Explain various types of nonsense literature.
10. Define certain literary terms.

VOCABULARY

Study these words to enhance your learning success in this section.

alliterative (u lit′ u rā tiv). Having words beginning with the same sound or letter.

anonymous (a non′ u mus). By or from a person whose name is not known or given.

articulation (är tik yü lā′ shun). Clear, distinct pronunciation of speech sounds.

coined (koind). Made up or invented.

jabberwocky (jab′ ur wok ē). Nonsensical talking or writing.

jingle (jing′ gul). Verse or song that has repetition of similar sounds; a catchy rhyme.

limerick (lim′ ur ik). A form of humorous nonsense verse of five lines.

nonsense (non′ sens). Foolish talk; words without meaning.

obstacle (ob′ stu kul). Something that stands in the way.

phonetic (fu net′ ik). Having to do with speech sounds.

pronunciation (pru nun sē ā′ shun). Making the sounds of a spoken language.

pseudonym (süd du nim). Pen name; fictitious name used by an author instead of his real name.

rhyme (rīm). Agreement in the final sounds of words or lines.

rhythm (riТН′ um). Regular repetition of beat or accent.

tongue twister (tung twis′ tur). Phrase or sentence that is difficult to say quickly without a mistake.

verse (vėrs). A form of poetry, usually somewhat lighter or more frivolous than serious poetry.

PRACTICE OF ACTUAL WORDS

Note: As you begin work on this section, you will need to have a good dictionary on your grade level. Study the section (usually in the front) of your dictionary that explains the **pronunciation** key used for the entry words.

However extensive your sight vocabulary may be, correct pronunciation is vital to effective communication. Whether you are giving a formal oral presentation before a large group, speaking informally among a smaller group of friends, or just listening actively and attentively to someone else speak, you need to master the skill of pronouncing words correctly.

If the English language is your native tongue, you may be surprised to learn that many **obstacles** to correct English pronunciation exist.

English is not a **phonetic** language. Explained simply, you cannot just look at all English words and "sound them out" from the way they are spelled. The word *phonetic* is just one example. The *ph* in *phonetic* is pronounced as an *f.*

Phonetic is pronounced fu net′ik.

Find these words in your dictionary. In the blank, copy the pronunciation for each word, complete with diacritical marks.

Example: Pharisee   <u>far´ u se</u>

3.1 pharmacy   _____

3.2 phone   _____

3.3 photograph   _____

3.4 phrase   _____

3.5 physics   _____

Many words in the English language contain one or more silent letters. Silent letters are often the result of "borrowing" words from other languages. Occasionally, however, the word's accepted pronunciation has simply changed over the years, and certain letters are no longer sounded when the word is spoken.

Find these words in your dictionary. In the blank, copy the pronunciation for each word, complete with diacritical marks. In the parentheses, write the silent letter or letters.

Example: gnome   a. _____ nōm _____   b. (g)

3.6 island   a. _____   b. (___)

3.7 debt   a. _____   b. (___)

3.8 knife   a. _____   b. (___)

3.9 salmon   a. _____   b. (___)

3.10 ghost   a. _____   b. (___)

3.11 light   a. _____   b. (___)

Some English words differ greatly in pronunciation and in spelling. You wonder how the written word can be the same word as the spoken word. See if your dictionary explains the history of the following word.

Find this word in your dictionary. Copy the pronunciation complete with diacritical markings.

3.12 colonel   _____

Frequently the same letter or combination of letters appearing in words of somewhat similar spelling will have quite different pronunciation.

Find the following words in your dictionary. Copy the pronunciation complete with diacritical marks.

Example: Chaldea _____kal dē´ u_____

3.13 chalk _____

3.14 charlatan _____

3.15 chasm _____

3.16 chassis _____

3.17 chauffeur _____

3.18 check _____

3.19 Christian _____

The same word may be pronounced differently depending upon the meaning or the part of speech.

Complete this exercise. The following ten pairs of words appear to be identical. The usage or the part of speech is given after each word. Find each word in your dictionary. Copy the pronunciation, complete with diacritical marks. Be sure to match the correct pronunciation to the correct word.

3.20 a. escort (noun) _____
     b. escort (verb) _____

3.21 a. produce (noun) _____
     b. produce (verb) _____

3.22 a. lead (noun) _____
     b. lead (verb) _____

3.23 a. rebel (noun or adj.) _____
     b. rebel (verb) _____

3.24 a. record (noun or adj.) _____
     b. record (verb) _____

3.25 a. refund (noun) _____
     b. refund (verb) _____

3.26 a. wind (noun) _____
     b. wind (verb) _____

3.27 a. combine (noun) _____
     b. combine (verb) _____

3.28 a. read (verb infinitive) _____
     b. read (verb past tense) _____

3.29 a. wound (noun) _____
     b. wound (as past tense of wind) _____

Complete this activity. Choose any five pairs of the preceding words. Demonstrate your understanding of the differences by using each word of the five pairs in a brief sentence. Indicate the part of speech as shown in the example.

Example: Listen to the *wind* blow! (noun)
Did you *wind* the clock? (verb)

3.30   a. _____
b. _____
3.31   a. _____
b. _____
3.32   a. _____
b. _____
3.33   a. _____
b. _____
3.34   a. _____
b. _____

How do you determine the correct pronunciation of a word? One answer, of course, is to consult a good, standard modern dictionary. Sometimes the dictionary will give two or more pronunciations for the same word expressing the same meaning. When a dictionary gives two or more pronunciations, the first pronunciation is not necessarily "more correct" than the others. Usually the first pronunciation is the most commonly accepted pronunciation, however.

Some words differ greatly in pronunciation from one region or part of the country to another. One pronunciation is not necessarily more correct than the other. If you still have doubts after looking in the dictionary, try to find out how an educated person in your community says the word.

Find the following words in your dictionary. Copy the two or more pronunciations, complete with diacritical marks. Circle the pronunciation that you believe is the commonly accepted choice where you live.

Example: rodeo   (rō´ dē ō, rō dā´ ō)

3.35   pecan   _____
3.36   route   _____
3.37   due   _____
3.38   lever   _____
3.39   tomato   _____
3.40   either   _____
3.41   coupon   _____
3.42   juvenile   _____
3.43   aunt   _____
3.44   laboratory   _____

Words encountered in reading. You may be convinced by now that correct pronunciation is vital to spoken communication. But you may think, when you are reading silently to yourself, that whether or not you can pronounce certain words is not important.

Yes, it is important. For one thing, the eye tends to skip over words that the silent reader cannot pronounce. Furthermore, a word that you cannot pronounce even silently in your own mind is a word you truly do not understand.

When you are asked to read aloud, the problem is compounded. Words that the eye skips over are words that the tongue stumbles over.

Perhaps nowhere are these twin problems more obvious than in reading from the Holy Bible.

The following fifty words were selected from the Gospel according to Mark. See how many of them you can pronounce correctly.

synagogue	ordained	marvelled	hypocrites
leprosy	surnamed	testimony	perceive
beseech	perish	tolerable	draught
publicans	rebuke	anointed	covetousness
physicians	asunder	convenient	impediment
marred	fetters	thither	fragments
sabbath	virtue	constrained	savour(est)
withered	tumult	toiling	raiment
plagues	damsel	besought	tabernacles
nought	scourge	spikenard	insurrection
gnash (eth)	alabaster	tarry	myrrh
millstone	ointment	staves	transgressor
centurion	sepulchre		

Complete the exercise.

3.45

With one or more classmates, quietly practice pronouncing the preceding fifty words. On a separate sheet of paper, write the words that are difficult for you to pronounce and those that are familiar to you. Look up those words in your dictionary. Copy the pronunciation, complete with diacritical marks. As an added learning aid, you may wish to write a brief definition of the words that are new to you.

Teacher check _____

                     Initial   Date

Complete this activity.

3.46

Select a favorite Bible passage. Read it aloud to yourself. If you cannot pronounce some words, you know how to learn the correct pronunciation. When you are sure that you can read the passage aloud, correctly and smoothly, ask your teacher to let you read aloud to her or to the class. Ask your classmates to listen for correct pronunciation. Be prepared to do the same for them.

Teacher check _____

                     Initial   Date

Words encountered in speaking. Some spoken words are mispronounced so often that they are frequently misspelled as well.

Sometimes the problem is that not all the letters are correctly pronounced when the word is spoken; therefore, those letters are accidentally left out when the word is spelled. An example is the word *government*. If the word is mispronounced as *goverment* (with the *n* left out) it is almost certain to be misspelled.

Sometimes the problem is a matter of substituting the sound of a letter that the word does not contain. An example is the word *escape*. If the word is mispronounced as *excape* (with the sound of an *x* substituted for the *s*) the word is bound to be misspelled.

Complete these activities. The words given have the incorrect spellings that frequently result from mispronunciation. In the blank, write the correctly spelled word. Then find the words in your dictionary. Copy the correct pronunciation complete with diacritical marks.

	Example:	goverment	a. __government__	b. __(guv´ urn munt)__
3.47		libery	a. _____	b. _____
3.48		histry	a. _____	b. _____
3.49		labatory	a. _____	b. _____
3.50		excape	a. _____	b. _____
3.51		suprise	a. _____	b. _____
3.52		warsh	a. _____	b. _____
3.53		sophmore	a. _____	b. _____
3.54		jography	a. _____	b. _____
3.55		mathmatics	a. _____	b. _____
3.56		litachure	a. _____	b. _____

Teacher check _____

                        Initial   Date

PRACTICE OF NONSENSE WORDS

Nonsense verse is a type of light verse. Nonsense verse is delightful to read because of its strong **rhythm** and because of its complete lack of logic or good sense. Nonsense verse is often composed of "made-up" or invented words that have no real meaning.

Some of the words and phrases are real **tongue twisters**. A tongue twister is a group of words, often **alliterative,** that is difficult to say quickly without a mistake. Many years ago, when schoolbooks were very scarce, tongue twisters and similar **jingles** were used to help children learn proper pronunciation.

Pronouncing tongue twisters is good practice for you. Besides being fun to say, they soon make pronouncing actual words and phrases seem simple by comparison.

The **limerick** is another form of nonsense verse. The name limerick is supposed to have come from the name of a city in Ireland.

Nonsense verse seems to be typically English and American. Not many examples are known to exist in other languages. Perhaps that fact is because English, as you have learned in this section, is not a phonetic language. Unlike the alphabets of some languages, the letters of the English language may be pronounced in many different ways.

When nonsense literature is mentioned, two English authors are sure to be named: Edward Lear and Lewis Carroll. (Lewis Carroll is a **pseudonym** for Charles L. Dodgson.)

Complete this activity.

3.57 Find these two authors of nonsense literature in an encyclopedia or other reference book. Do not copy the entries. Rather, summarize what you learn in a few sentences about each.

a. Edward Lear _____

_____

_____

_____

_____

_____

_____

b. Lewis Carroll _____

_____

_____

_____

_____

_____

_____

Teacher check _____

Initial   Date

47

One of the most popular examples of nonsense verse is "Jabberwocky," by Lewis Carroll. The poem contains many made-up words, such as *brillig* and *toves* and *mimsy*. Can you find these words in your dictionary? Probably not. You may find the word **jabberwocky**, however. Even though Lewis Carroll **coined** the word, it has found its way into our language. Notice the nonsense words in the two following selections.

Jabberwocky

'Twas brillig, and the slithy toves
    Did gyre and gimble in the wabe;
All mimsy were the borogoves,
    And the mome raths outgrabe.

"Beware the Jabberwock, my son!
    The jaws that bite, the claws that catch!
Beware the Jubjub bird, and shun
    The frumious Bandersnatch!"

He took his vorpal sword in hand:
    Long time the manxome foe he sought—
So rested he by the Tumtum tree,
    And stood a while in thought.

And as in uffish thought he stood,
    The jabberwock, with eyes of flame,
Came whiffling through the tulgey wood,
    And burbled as it came!

One, two! One, two! And through and through
    The vorpal blade went snicker-snack
He left it dead, and with its head
    He went galumphing back.

"And hast thou slain the Jabberwock?
    Come to my arms, my beamish boy!
O frabjous day! Callooh! Callay!"
    He chortled in his joy.

'Twas brillig, and the slithy toves
    Did gyre and gimble in the wabe;
All mimsy were the borogoves,
    And the mome raths outgrabe.

—Lewis Carroll

The Owl and the Pussy-cat

I

The Owl and the Pussy-cat went to sea
   In a beautiful pea-green boat,
They took some honey, and plenty of money,
   Wrapped up in a five-pound note.
The Owl looked up to the stars above,
   And sang to a small guitar,
'O lovely Pussy! O Pussy, my love,
   What a beautiful Pussy you are,
     You are,
     You are!
   What a beautiful Pussy you are!'

II

Pussy said to the Owl, 'You elegant fowl!
   How charmingly sweet you sing!
O let us be married! too long we have tarried:
   But what shall we do for a ring?'
They sailed away, for a year and a day,
   To the land where the Bong-tree grows
And there in a wood a Piggy-wig stood
   With a ring at the end of his nose,
     His nose,
     His nose,
   With a ring at the end of his nose.

III

'Dear Pig, are you willing to sell for one shilling
   Your ring?' Said the Piggy, 'I will.'
So they took it away, and were married next day
   By the turkey who lives on the hill.
They dined on mince, and slices of quince,
   Which they ate with a runcible spoon;
And hand in hand, on the edge of the sand,
   They danced by the light of the moon,
     The moon,
     The moon,
   They danced by the light of the moon.

—Edward Lear

Although Edward Lear did not invent the limerick verse, he did much to make the limerick popular. Many limericks, however, are **anonymous**; that is, the true author is unknown.

Limericks

There was an Old Man with a beard,
Who said, 'It is just as I feared!—
    Two Owls and a Hen,
    Four Larks and a Wren,
Have all built their nest in my beard!'

            —Edward Lear

There was an Old Man in a tree,
Who was horribly bored by a Bee;
    When they said, 'Does it buzz?'
    He replied, 'Yes, it does!'
'It's a regular brute of a Bee!'

            —Edward Lear

There was an Old Man in a boat,
Who said, 'I'm afloat! I'm afloat!'
    When they said, 'No! you ain't!'
    He was ready to faint,
That unhappy old man in a boat.

            —Edward Lear

There was an Old Man who said, 'How
Shall I flee from this horrible Cow?
    I will sit on this stile,
    And continue to smile,
Which may soften the heart of that Cow.'

—Edward Lear

The limerick follows a strict form. A limerick has five lines. The first two lines **rhyme** with the last line. The third and fourth lines are shorter than the other three. They rhyme with each other.

Complete this activity. Find a book in your school or public library containing limericks. Select one that is appropriate for reading aloud. Copy it here. Be sure that you can pronounce all the words. Be prepared to read the limerick aloud to the class.

3.58

_____

_____

_____

_____

_____

_____

_____

3.59   **OPTIONAL ACTIVITY:** Your teacher may ask the class to divide into small groups of four or five and try writing your own original limerick. Do not be afraid to try. It can be great fun! Remember, a limerick is meant to be amusing; it is not serious poetry.

Teacher check _____

                        Initial   Date

Tongue Twisters

Peter Piper picked a peck of pickled peppers;
Did Peter Piper pick a peck of pickled peppers?
If Peter Piper picked a peck of pickled peppers,
Where's the peck of pickled peppers Peter Piper picked?

★ ★ ★

She sells sea shells by the sea shore.

★ ★ ★

Jumping Jackey jeered a jesting juggler.

★ ★ ★

A visibly vicious vulture wrote some verses to a
veal-cutlet in a volume bound in vellum.

★ ★ ★

Bob borrowed Betty's blue bank book but forgot
to bring it back.

★ ★ ★

Can cats carry kittens in cardboard containers,
considering how careful cats can be?

★ ★ ★

Billy Button bought a buttered biscuit.

★ ★ ★

A singing seal sat sunning itself on the silvery
sparkling sands of Sicily.

★ ★ ★

An egotistical eagle named Elmer elected to elevate
himself to the eastern edge of Mount Elbrus.

Selected Reading List

The following list contains the authors and titles of nonsense or
humorous writings that you may enjoy. Ask your teacher or your
school librarian or public librarian to help you locate these writings or
to make other suggestions.

"The Blind Men and the Elephant," by John Godfrey Saxe.
"The Cats of Kilkenny." (Anonymous)
"Humpty Dumpty's Recitation," by Lewis Carroll.
"The Owl Critic," by Thomas Field.
"The Quangle Wangle's Hat," by Edward Lear.
"The Skippery Boo," by Earl L. Newton.
"The Walrus and the Carpenter," by Lewis Carroll.

Alice's Adventures in Wonderland, by Lewis Carroll.
The Birds and the Beasts Were There, by William Cole.
The Complete Nonsense Book, by Edward Lear.
Laughing Time, by William Jay Smith.
A Little Laughter, edited by Walter Lorraine.
Oh, How Ridiculous! by William Cole.
Oh, How Silly! by William Cole.
Pocketful of Rhymes, edited by Katherine Love.
Through the Looking Glass, by Lewis Carroll.
Tirra Lira, by Laura E. Richards.
Tongue Tanglers, by Charles Francis Potter.
A Twister of Twisters, a Tangle of Tongues, by Alvin Schwartz.

 Complete this activity. Find the following words in your dictionary. (You may have to consult more than one.)
a. Copy the pronunciation, complete with diacritical marks. Note those that are actual words and those that have been coined.
b. Write a brief definition.

3.60   chortle   a. _____   b. _____
        galumph   a. _____   b. _____
        peck (unit of measure) a. _____   b. _____
        pound (unit of money)   a. _____   b. _____
        runcible spoon   a. _____   b. _____
        shilling   a. _____   b. _____
        stile   a. _____   b. _____
        vellum   a. _____   b. _____

 Write the letter of the correct answer.

3.61   A pen name used by an author instead of his real name is a _____ .
        a. anonymous   c. pseudonym
        b. homonym   d. pseudopod
3.62   Agreement in the final sounds of words or lines is _____ .
        a. rhythm   c. measure
        b. rhyme   d. verse
3.63   A sentence that is difficult to say quickly is a _____ .
        a. tall tale   c. tongue twister
        b. limerick   d. nursery rhyme
3.64   Verse with foolish words having no serious meaning is called _____ .
        a. free verse   c. runcible
        b. rhythmetical   d. nonsense

3.65	Words that have the same first letter or sound are _____ .
	a. limerick	c. rhymed
	b. alliterative	d. coined

3.65   Words that have the same first letter or sound are _____ .
         a. limerick   c. rhymed
         b. alliterative   d. coined

3.66   A word that is made up or invented is called a _____ word.
         a. coined   c. vellum
         b. shilling   d. tongue twister

3.67   A form of humorous verse, usually containing five lines, is called a(n) _____ .
         a. limerick   c. alliterative
         b. rhythm   d. pseudonym

3.68   The regular repetition of a strong beat or accent is called _____ .
         a. rhyme   c. rhythm
         b. limerick   d. alliteration

SPELLING

The words in Spelling Words-3 are often misspelled because they are often casually or incorrectly pronounced. As you study these words, be sure that you learn the correct pronunciation.

──────── Spelling Words - 3 ────────

stomach	coupon	suspicion
athletics	escape	borrow
attacked	again	yesterday
iron	height	February
library	having	wash
drowned	often	rinse
surprise	tired	wrench
government	children	graduate

Complete the following activity. Find each spelling word in your dictionary. Copy the correct pronunciation. Notice that the pronunciation may differ from the spelling.

3.69	again	_____
3.70	athletics	_____
3.71	attacked	_____
3.72	borrow	_____
3.73	children	_____
3.74	coupon	_____
3.75	drowned	_____
3.76	escape	_____
3.77	February	_____

3.78	government	_____
3.79	graduate	_____
3.80	having	_____
3.81	height	_____
3.82	iron	_____
3.83	library	_____
3.84	often	_____
3.85	rinse	_____
3.86	stomach	_____
3.87	surprise	_____
3.88	suspicion	_____
3.89	tired	_____
3.90	wash	_____
3.91	wrench	_____
3.92	yesterday	_____

Complete the activity. Write five "nonsense" sentences, using as many of the words from Spelling Words-3 in each as you can. Underline words from the list.

Example: Since <u>yesterday</u> was the first of <u>February</u>, the <u>government</u>, in a <u>surprise</u> move, ordered all <u>tired children</u> to <u>borrow</u> a <u>library coupon</u> before they can <u>wash</u> and <u>rinse</u> an <u>iron wrench</u>.

3.93 _____

_____

3.94 _____

_____

3.95 _____

_____

3.96 _____

_____

3.97 _____

_____

_____

Ask your teacher to give you a practice spelling test of Spelling Words-3. Restudy the words you missed.

Teacher check _____

Initial   Date

Before you take this last Self Test, you may want to do one or more of these self checks.

1. _____ Read the objectives. Determine if you can do them.

2. _____ Restudy the material related to any objectives that you cannot do.

3. _____ Use the SQ3R study procedure to review the material:

    a. **S**can the sections.

    b. **Q**uestion yourself again (review the questions you wrote initially).

    c. **R**ead to answer your questions.

    d. **R**ecite the answers to yourself.

    e. **R**eview areas you didn't understand.

4. _____ Review all vocabulary, activities, and Self Tests, writing a correct answer for each wrong answer.

SELF TEST 3

Match these terms (each answer, 2 points).

3.01 _____ declarative		a. helping
3.02 _____ fragment		b purpose
3.03 _____ indention		c. group of sentences about one topic
3.04 _____ paragraph		d. short, lively story
3.05 _____ coined words		e. incomplete part of a sentence
3.06 _____ irrelevant		f. not to the point
3.07 _____ auxiliary		g. several main clauses joined by excessive *and's* or *so's*
3.08 _____ anecdote		h. a sentence asking a question
3.09 _____ run-on		i. words that are made up or invented
3.010 _____ interrogative		j. end punctuation
		k. an abstract idea
		l. sentences that state or tell something
		m. signals the beginning of each new paragraph

Answer *true* **or** *false* (each answer, 1 point).

3.011 _____ Dictionaries are all arranged the same way.

3.012 _____ When the dictionary gives two or more pronunciations for the same word, only the first is considered correct.

3.013 _____ If an author does not wish to use his real name, he may use a pseudonym.

3.014 _____ "Coined" words do not appear in any dictionary.

3.015 _____ "Nonsense" verse is actually intended to be serious.

3.016 _____ Lewis Carroll's real name was Charles L. Dodgson.

3.017 _____ English is not a phonetic language.

3.018 _____ A paragraph must contain only one central idea or the words of only one speaker.

3.019 _____ Paragraphs in fiction books and stories are least likely to contain topic sentences.

3.020 _____ A transition paragraph often helps to show a change in scene, season, or characters.

Complete the following statements (each answer, 3 points).

3.021 A pen name used by an author instead of his real name is a

_____ .

3.022 Agreement in the final sounds of words or lines is _____ .

3.023 A sentence that is difficult to say quickly is a _____ .

3.024 Verse that includes foolish words and that has no serious meaning is called _____ verse.

3.025 Words that have the same first letter or sound are _____ .

3.026 A word that is made up or invented is _____ .

3.027 A form of humorous verse, usually containing five lines, is a

_____ .

3.028 The regular repetition of a strong beat or accent is _____ .

3.029 When all the sentences in a paragraph support the topic sentence, it is said to have _____ .

3.030 The logical progression of facts or ideas is called _____ .

Define these items (each answer, 4 points).

3.031 function _____

_____

3.032 tangible _____

_____

3.033 deductive _____

_____

3.034 summation _____

_____

3.035 transition _____

_____

Match these items to their sentence types (each answer, 2 points).

3.036 _____ Tommy is stuck in the tree!   a. declarative
3.037 _____ Please bring that here!   b. exclamatory
3.038 _____ Saul of Tarsus was an enemy   c. interrogative
              of all Christians.   d. imperative
3.039 _____ Will you close the door?
3.040 _____ The house is on fire!

```
72
   / 90
```

Score _____
Teacher check _____
              Initial   Date

Take your spelling test of Spelling Words-3.

Before taking the LIFEPAC Test, you may want to do one or more of these self checks.

1. _____ Read the objectives. Check to see if you can do them.
2. _____ Restudy the material related to any objectives that you cannot do.
3. _____ Use the SQ3R study procedure to review the material.
4. _____ Review activities, Self Tests, and LIFEPAC vocabulary words.
5. _____ Restudy areas of weakness indicated by the last Self Test.
6. _____ Review all Spelling Words in this LIFEPAC.